17

Usborne
First Activities

Summer Fun

Fiona Watt

Illustrated by Katie Lovell

Photographs by Howard Allman

Digital manipulation by Nick Wakeford

Salty sea picture

  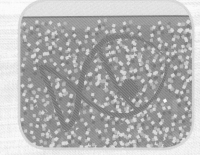

1. Paint a piece of thick blue paper with lots of white glue.

2. Sprinkle the glue with some fine glitter and lots of salt.

3. When the glue is dry, draw a fish with bright pink chalk.

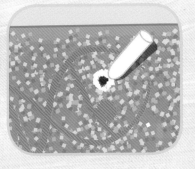

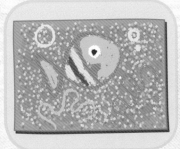

4. Draw a blue eye, then draw around it with white chalk.

5. Then, use red, green and yellow chalks to fill in the fish's body.

6. Draw some big bubbles and seaweed around your fish.

Ice-cream cone

Use light brown paper.

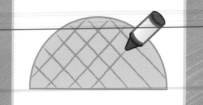

Hold the cone while the glue dries.

1. Draw around a plate on a piece of paper. Cut out the circle, then cut it in half.

2. Use a brown crayon to draw crisscross lines on the paper, like this.

3. Bend the paper around to make a cone shape and glue it in place.

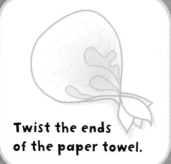

Twist the ends of the paper towel.

Stand the ice cream in a mug until it is dry.

4. To make the ice cream, scrunch some paper towels into a ball. Then, wrap another one around the ball.

5. Glue the ball inside the cone. Then, mix some thick paint with white glue in an old container.

6. Brush the mixture all over the ice cream. Then, sprinkle glitter over the wet paint.

This ice cream had dark
pink paint dribbled over
it for raspberry sauce.

This ice cream
had little beads
sprinkled onto it.

You could cut
a flag from
patterned paper
to glue at the top
of the sandcastle.

Printed sandcastle

Use thick paint.

Turn the sponge on its side to print the second rectangle.

Keep the strip for later.

1. Spread some yellow and orange paints on an old plate.

2. Dip a sponge into the yellow paint and print two rectangles.

3. Cut a strip off the end of the sponge, then print a turret.

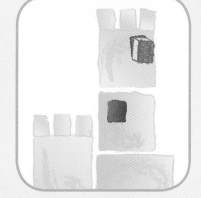

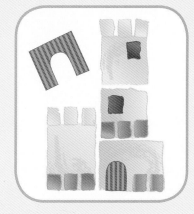

4. Cut the end off the strip and print yellow squares for battlements.

5. Dip the same sponge into the orange paint and print two windows.

6. Print some pale orange squares for decoration. Then, cut a paper door and glue it on.

Kite collage

1. Cut two squares of paper. Glue them onto a big square, like this.

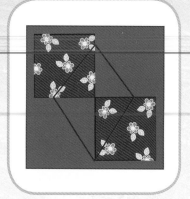

2. Draw a kite in the middle of the paper. Then, cut it out.

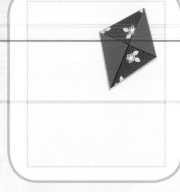

3. Glue the kite at the top corner of another piece of paper.

4. Cut a piece of string and glue it on in a wiggly line, coming from the bottom of the kite.

5. Cut some thin strips of material and tie a knot in the middle of each one.

Trim the strips to make them the same size.

6. Trim the ends of the strips, then glue them along the string.

You could decorate
your kite by gluing
on an old button.

You could use
paper to make
the stem, leaves
and petals, if you
don't have a pipe
cleaner or felt.

Big sunflower

Let the paint dry.

1. Paint the back of two paper plates with red and brown paint.

2. For a stem, glue a pipe cleaner onto a piece of thick paper.

3. Cut the red plate into a pot shape. Glue it over the stem, like this.

4. Cut lots of petals from yellow felt. Cut two green leaves, too.

5. Turn the brown plate over and glue the petals around the edge of the plate.

6. Glue the leaves on either side of the stem. Then, glue the flower on top.

Busy bumble bees

1. Cut an oval for a bee's body from yellow material.

2. Cut two teardrop shapes for wings from silver foil.

3. Glue the bee's body and wings onto a piece of blue paper, like this.

4. Paint two dark stripes on the body. Then, add eyes, legs and antennae, too.

5. Glue some old beads onto the antennae. Then, use pens to draw a happy face.

You could use paper instead of material for the bee's body.

If you don't have any beads, you could glue on buttons or balls of silver foil.

Happy crab

You could paint a
sandy background
for your crab.

1. Draw an oval
for a crab's body
with an orange
crayon.

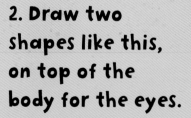

2. Draw two
shapes like this,
on top of the
body for the eyes.

3. Then, draw two
large claws beside
the eyes. Add some
lines on the claws.

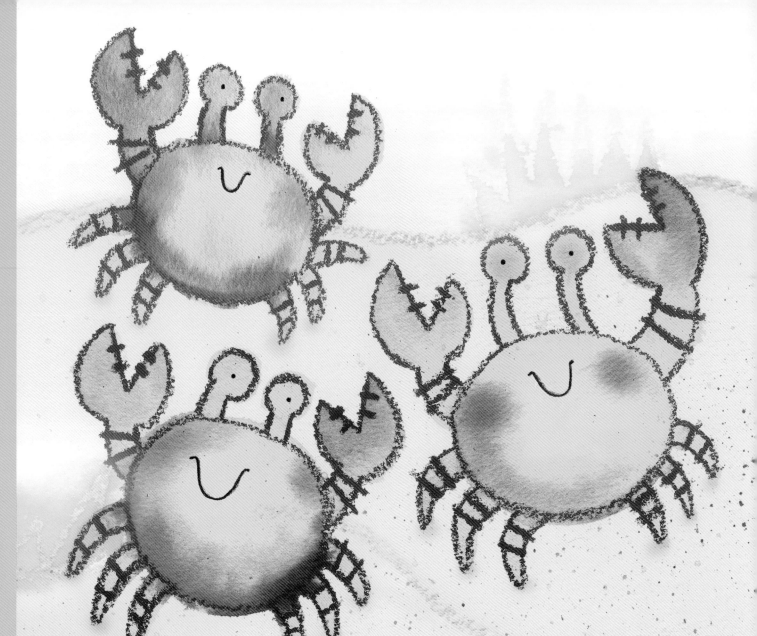

Let the paints mix together.

4. Add some little legs below the body, and draw lines on them, too.

5. Fill in the crab with watery orange and pink paints.

6. When the paint is dry, draw little dots for eyes and add a smiling mouth.

Sparkly Shell

1. Paint a piece of paper with white glue. Let it dry.

2. Mix some thick bright paint with some more glue.

3. Quickly paint a shell shape on the paper.

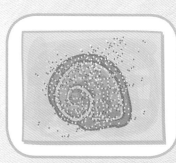

4. Use the end of the brush to scratch lines into the wet paint.

5. Sprinkle the shell with fine glitter. Shake off any extra glitter when the paint is dry.

Use the ideas on these pages for different shapes of shells.

To make a pearl, sprinkle a blob of glue with glitter. Let it dry, then cut it out and glue it on.

Beach hut hanging

1. Cut a piece of white cardboard and punch holes in the top corners.

Use a hole puncher.

2. Use a sponge to print a patch of yellow paint on the cardboard.

3. Cut three shapes for huts from different bright papers.

Cut a little window, too.

Leave the glue to dry.

4. Cut triangles and strips for the roofs, and some little rectangles for doors.

5. Cut a circle for a sun. Then, glue all the shapes onto the cardboard.

6. Tie thick string through the holes, like this, for hanging your picture.

18

You could make another picture
and tie it below, like this.

Paper boat

You could make a pirate to put in your boat.

1. Cut a rectangle from an old newspaper and fold it in half.

Folded edge

2. Fold the top corners down so that they meet in the middle.

3. Then, fold up the top layer of the paper at the bottom, like this.

20

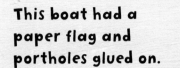

This boat had a
paper flag and
portholes glued on.

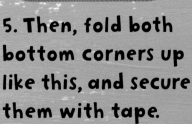

4. Turn the paper
over and fold up
the paper at the
bottom, again.

5. Then, fold both
bottom corners up
like this, and secure
them with tape.

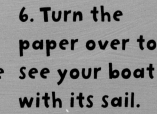

6. Turn the
paper over to
see your boat
with its sail.

21

Strawberries

You could draw some insects hiding in the leaves.

Add some grass, too.

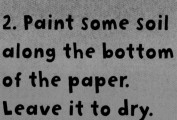

1. Paint several stems, like these, on a piece of thick paper.

2. Paint some soil along the bottom of the paper. Leave it to dry.

3. Draw a shape for a strawberry on red paper. Add dots for seeds.

You could add
white strawberries
that aren't ripe yet.

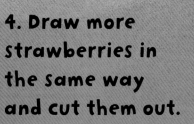

4. Draw more
strawberries in
the same way
and cut them out.

5. Cut out some
green leaves
using paper from
old magazines.

6. Glue a strawberry
onto the end of
each stem. Glue
the leaves on, too.

Summer sandals

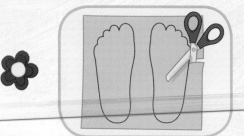

1. Draw around your feet. Cut out the shapes.

2. Make a cut beside each big toe, like this.

3. Cut four pieces of ribbon. Slot them between the toes.

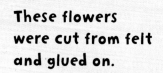

These flowers were cut from felt and glued on.

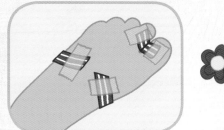

4. Wrap the ribbon around the sides of each foot. Tape the ends onto the back.

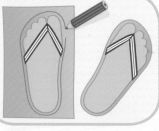

5. Glue the feet onto another piece of paper. Draw around each foot and cut them out.

You could add sequins for decoration.

24